Friends & Family
ORGANISER

Illustrated by Juliette Clarke

A HELEN EXLEY GIFTBOOK

Name	Name
Address	Address
Telephone	Telephone
Mob	Mobile
E-Mail	E-Mail
Name	Name
Address	Address
Telephone	Telephone
Mob	Mobile
E-Mail	E-Mail
Name	Name
Address	Address
Telephone	Telephone
Mob	Mobile
E-Mail	E-Mail

Name

Address

Telephone

Mob

E-Mail

Name

Address

Telephone

Mob

E-Mail

Name

Address

Telephone

Mob

E-Mail

Name

Address

Telephone

Mobile

E-Mail

Name

Address

Telephone

Mobile

E-Mail

Name

Address

Telephone

Mobile

E-Mail

Name

Address

Telephone

Mob

E-Mail

Name

Address

Telephone

Mob

E-Mail

Name

Address

Telephone

Mob

E-Mail

Name

Address

Telephone

Mobile

E-Mail

Name

Address

Telephone

Mobile

E-Mail

Name

Address

Telephone

Mobile

E-Mail

Name

Address

Telephone

Mob

E-Mail

Name

Address

Telephone

Mob

E-Mail

Name

Address

Telephone

Mobile

E-Mail

Name

Address

Telephone

Mobile

E-Mail

Name

Address

Telephone

Mobile

E-Mail

Name

Address

Telephone

Mob

E-Mail

Name

Address

Telephone

Mob

E-Mail

Name

Address

Telephone

Mob

E-Mail

Name

Address

Telephone

Mobile

E-Mail

Name

Address

Telephone

Mobile

E-Mail

Name

Address

Telephone

Mobile

E-Mail

Name

Address

Telephone

Mob

E-Mail

Name

Address

Telephone

Mob

E-Mail

Name

Address

Telephone

Mob

E-Mail

Name

Address

Telephone

Mobile

E-Mail

Name

Address

Telephone

Mobile

E-Mail

Name

Address

Telephone

Mobile

E-Mail

Name

Address

Telephone

Mob

E-Mail

Name

Address

Telephone

Mob

E-Mail

Name

Address

Telephone

Mobile

E-Mail

Name

Address

Telephone

Mobile

E-Mail

Name

Address

Telephone

Mob

E-Mail

Name

Address

Telephone

Mob

E-Mail

Name

Address

Telephone

Mob

E-Mail

Name

Address

Telephone

Mobile

E-Mail

Name

Address

Telephone

Mobile

E-Mail

Name

Address

Telephone

Mobile

E-Mail

Name

Address

Telephone

Mob

E-Mail

Name

Address

Telephone

Mob

E-Mail

Name

Address

Telephone

Mob

E-Mail

Name

Address

Telephone

Mobile

E-Mail

Name

Address

Telephone

Mobile

E-Mail

Name

Address

Telephone

Mobile

E-Mail

Name

Address

Telephone

Mob

E-Mail

Name

Address

Telephone

Mob

E-Mail

Name

Address

Telephone

Mob

E-Mail

Name

Address

Telephone

Mobile

E-Mail

Name

Address

Telephone

Mobile

E-Mail

Name

Address

Telephone

Mobile

E-Mail

Name

Address

Telephone

Mob

E-Mail

Name

Address

Telephone

Mob

E-Mail

Name

Address

Telephone

Mob

E-Mail

Name

Address

Telephone

Mobile

E-Mail

Name

Address

Telephone

Mobile

E-Mail

Name

Address

Telephone

Mobile

E-Mail

Name

Address

Telephone

Mob

E-Mail

Name

Address

Telephone

Mobile

E-Mail

Name

Address

Telephone

Mob

E-Mail

Name

Address

Telephone

Mobile

E-Mail

Name

Address

Telephone

Mob

E-Mail

Name

Address

Telephone

Mob

E-Mail

Name

Address

Telephone

Mob

E-Mail

Name

Address

Telephone

Mobile

E-Mail

Name

Address

Telephone

Mobile

E-Mail

Name

Address

Telephone

Mobile

E-Mail

Name

Address

Telephone

Mob

E-Mail

Name

Address

Telephone

Mob

E-Mail

Name

Address

Telephone

Mobile

E-Mail

Name

Address

Telephone

Mobile

E-Mail

Name

Address

Telephone

Mobile

E-Mail

Name

Address

Telephone

Mob

E-Mail

Name

Address

Telephone

Mob

E-Mail

Name

Address

Telephone

Mob

E-Mail

Name

Address

Telephone

Mobile

E-Mail

Name

Address

Telephone

Mobile

E-Mail

Name	Name
Address	Address
Telephone	Telephone
Mob	Mobile
E-Mail	E-Mail
Name	Name
Address	Address
Telephone	Telephone
Mob	Mobile
E-Mail	E-Mail
Name	Name
Address	Address
Telephone	Telephone
Mob	Mobile
E-Mail	E-Mail

Name

Address

Telephone

Mob

E-Mail

Name

Address

Telephone

Mob

E-Mail

Name

Address

Telephone

Mob

E-Mail

Name

Address

Telephone

Mobile

E-Mail

Name

Address

Telephone

Mobile

E-Mail

Name

Address

Telephone

Mobile

E-Mail

Name	Name
Address	Address
Telephone	Telephone
Mob	Mobile
E-Mail	E-Mail
Name	Name
Address	Address
Telephone	Telephone
Mob	Mobile
E-Mail	E-Mail
Name	Name
Address	Address
Telephone	Telephone
Mob	Mobile
E-Mail	E-Mail

Name

Address

Telephone

Mob

E-Mail

Name

Address

Telephone

Mob

E-Mail

Name

Address

Telephone

Mob

E-Mail

Name

Address

Telephone

Mobile

E-Mail

Name

Address

Telephone

Mobile

E-Mail

Name

Address

Telephone

Mobile

E-Mail

Name

Address

Telephone

Mob

E-Mail

Name

Address

Telephone

Mob

E-Mail

Name

Address

Telephone

Mob

E-Mail

Name

Address

Telephone

Mobile

E-Mail

Name

Address

Telephone

Mobile

E-Mail

Name

Address

Telephone

Mobile

E-Mail

Name	Name
Address	Address
Telephone	Telephone
Mob	Mobile
E-Mail	E-Mail
Name	Name
Address	Address
Telephone	Telephone
Mob	Mobile
E-Mail	E-Mail
Name	Name
Address	Address
Telephone	Telephone
Mob	Mobile
E-Mail	E-Mail

Name

Address

Telephone

Mob

E-Mail

Name

Address

Telephone

Mob

E-Mail

Name

Address

Telephone

Mob

E-Mail

Name

Address

Telephone

Mobile

E-Mail

Name

Address

Telephone

Mobile

E-Mail

Name

Address

Telephone

Mobile

E-Mail

Name	Name
Address	Address
Telephone	Telephone
Mob	Mobile
E-Mail	E-Mail
Name	Name
Address	Address
Telephone	Telephone
Mob	Mobile
E-Mail	E-Mail
Name	Name
Address	Address
Telephone	Telephone
Mob	Mobile
E-Mail	E-Mail

Name

Address

Telephone

Mob

E-Mail

Name

Address

Telephone

Mob

E-Mail

Name

Address

Telephone

Mob

E-Mail

Name

Address

Telephone

Mobile

E-Mail

Name

Address

Telephone

Mobile

E-Mail

Name

Address

Telephone

Mobile

E-Mail

Name

Address

Telephone

Mob

E-Mail

Name

Address

Telephone

Mob

E-Mail

Name

Address

Telephone

Mob

E-Mail

Name

Address

Telephone

Mobile

E-Mail

Name

Address

Telephone

Mobile

E-Mail

Name

Address

Telephone

Mobile

E-Mail

L

Name

Address

Telephone

Mob

E-Mail

Name

Address

Telephone

Mobile

E-Mail

Name

Address

Telephone

Mob

E-Mail

Name

Address

Telephone

Mobile

E-Mail

Name

Address

Telephone

Mob

E-Mail

Name

Address

Telephone

Mobile

E-Mail

M

Name

Address

Telephone

Mob

E-Mail

Name

Address

Telephone

Mob

E-Mail

Name

Address

Telephone

Mob

E-Mail

Name

Address

Telephone

Mobile

E-Mail

Name

Address

Telephone

Mobile

E-Mail

Name

Address

Telephone

Mobile

E-Mail

Name

Address

Telephone

Mob

E-Mail

Name

Address

Telephone

Mob

E-Mail

Name

Address

Telephone

Mob

E-Mail

Name

Address

Telephone

Mobile

E-Mail

Name

Address

Telephone

Mobile

E-Mail

Name

Address

Telephone

Mobile

E-Mail

NO

Name

Address

Telephone

Mob

E-Mail

Name

Address

Telephone

Mob

E-Mail

Name

Address

Telephone

Mobile

E-Mail

Name

Address

Telephone

Mobile

E-Mail

Name

Address

Telephone

Mobile

E-Mail

Name

Address

Telephone

Mob

E-Mail

Name

Address

Telephone

Mob

E-Mail

Name

Address

Telephone

Mob

E-Mail

Name

Address

Telephone

Mobile

E-Mail

Name

Address

Telephone

Mobile

E-Mail

Name

Address

Telephone

Mobile

E-Mail

Name	Name
Address	Address
Telephone	Telephone
Mob	Mobile
E-Mail	E-Mail
Name	Name
Address	Address
Telephone	Telephone
Mob	Mobile
E-Mail	E-Mail
Name	Name
Address	Address
Telephone	Telephone
Mob	Mobile
E-Mail	E-Mail

Name	Name
Address	Address
Telephone	Telephone
Mob	Mobile
E-Mail	E-Mail
Name	Name
Address	Address
Telephone	Telephone
Mob	Mobile
E-Mail	E-Mail
Name	Name
Address	Address
Telephone	Telephone
Mob	Mobile
E-Mail	E-Mail

P

Name	Name
Address	Address
Telephone	Telephone
Mob	Mobile
E-Mail	E-Mail
Name	Name
Address	Address
Telephone	Telephone
Mob	Mobile
E-Mail	E-Mail
Name	Name
Address	Address
Telephone	Telephone
Mob	Mobile
E-Mail	E-Mail

QR

Name

Address

Telephone

Mob

E-Mail

Name

Address

Telephone

Mob

E-Mail

Name

Address

Telephone

Mob

E-Mail

Name

Address

Telephone

Mobile

E-Mail

Name

Address

Telephone

Mobile

E-Mail

Name

Address

Telephone

Mobile

E-Mail

Name

Address

Telephone

Mob

E-Mail

Name

Address

Telephone

Mob

E-Mail

Name

Address

Telephone

Mobile

E-Mail

Name

Address

Telephone

Mobile

E-Mail

Name

Address

Telephone

Mobile

E-Mail

QR

Name

Address

Telephone

Mob

E-Mail

Name

Address

Telephone

Mob

E-Mail

Name

Address

Telephone

Mob

E-Mail

Name

Address

Telephone

Mobile

E-Mail

Name

Address

Telephone

Mobile

E-Mail

Name

Address

Telephone

Mobile

E-Mail

Name	Name
Address	Address
Telephone	Telephone
Mob	Mobile
E-Mail	E-Mail

Name	Name
Address	Address
Telephone	Telephone
Mob	Mobile
E-Mail	E-Mail

S

Name

Address

Telephone

Mob

E-Mail

Name

Address

Telephone

Mob

E-Mail

Name

Address

Telephone

Mob

E-Mail

Name

Address

Telephone

Mobile

E-Mail

Name

Address

Telephone

Mobile

E-Mail

Name

Address

Telephone

Mobile

E-Mail

Name

Address

Telephone

Mob

E-Mail

Name

Address

Telephone

Mob

E-Mail

Name

Address

Telephone

Mob

E-Mail

Name

Address

Telephone

Mobile

E-Mail

Name

Address

Telephone

Mobile

E-Mail

Name

Address

Telephone

Mobile

E-Mail

S

Name	Name
Address	Address
Telephone	Telephone
Mob	Mobile
E-Mail	E-Mail
Name	Name
Address	Address
Telephone	Telephone
Mob	Mobile
E-Mail	E-Mail
Name	Name
Address	Address
Telephone	Telephone
Mob	Mobile
E-Mail	E-Mail

S

Name

Address

Telephone

Mob

E-Mail

Name

Address

Telephone

Mob

E-Mail

Name

Address

Telephone

Mob

E-Mail

Name

Address

Telephone

Mobile

E-Mail

Name

Address

Telephone

Mobile

E-Mail

Name

Address

Telephone

Mobile

E-Mail

Name

Address

Telephone

Mob

E-Mail

Name

Address

Telephone

Mob

E-Mail

Name

Address

Telephone

Mobile

E-Mail

Name

Address

Telephone

Mobile

E-Mail

Name

Address

Telephone

Mobile

E-Mail

T

Name

Address

Telephone

Mob

E-Mail

Name

Address

Telephone

Mobile

E-Mail

Name

Address

Telephone

Mob

E-Mail

Name

Address

Telephone

Mobile

E-Mail

Name	Name
Address	Address
Telephone	Telephone
Mob	Mobile
E-Mail	E-Mail

Name	Name
Address	Address
Telephone	Telephone
Mob	Mobile
E-Mail	E-Mail

Name	Name
Address	Address
Telephone	Telephone
Mob	Mobile
E-Mail	E-Mail

T

Name

Address

Telephone

Mob

E-Mail

Name

Address

Telephone

Mob

E-Mail

Name

Address

Telephone

Mob

E-Mail

Name

Address

Telephone

Mobile

E-Mail

Name

Address

Telephone

Mobile

E-Mail

Name

Address

Telephone

Mobile

E-Mail

Name

Address

Telephone

Mob

E-Mail

Name

Address

Telephone

Mobile

E-Mail

Name

Address

Telephone

Mob

E-Mail

Name

Address

Telephone

Mobile

E-Mail

T

Name

Address

Telephone

Mob

E-Mail

Name

Address

Telephone

Mob

E-Mail

Name

Address

Telephone

Mob

E-Mail

Name

Address

Telephone

Mobile

E-Mail

Name

Address

Telephone

Mobile

E-Mail

Name

Address

Telephone

Mobile

E-Mail

Name	Name
Address	Address
Telephone	Telephone
Mob	Mobile
E-Mail	E-Mail
Name	Name
Address	Address
Telephone	Telephone
Mob	Mobile
E-Mail	E-Mail
Name	Name
Address	Address
Telephone	Telephone
Mob	Mobile
E-Mail	E-Mail

UVW

Name

Address

Telephone

Mob

E-Mail

Name

Address

Telephone

Mob

E-Mail

Name

Address

Telephone

Mob

E-Mail

Name

Address

Telephone

Mobile

E-Mail

Name

Address

Telephone

Mobile

E-Mail

Name

Address

Telephone

Mobile

E-Mail

Name	Name
Address	Address
Telephone	Telephone
Mob	Mobile
E-Mail	E-Mail

Name	Name
Address	Address
Telephone	Telephone
Mob	Mobile
E-Mail	E-Mail

	Name
	Address
	Telephone
	Mobile
	E-Mail

UVW

Name	Name
Address	Address
Telephone	Telephone
Mob	Mobile
E-Mail	E-Mail

Name	Name
Address	Address
Telephone	Telephone
Mob	Mobile
E-Mail	E-Mail

Name	Name
Address	Address
Telephone	Telephone
Mob	Mobile
E-Mail	E-Mail

UVW

Name

Address

Telephone

Mob

E-Mail

Name

Address

Telephone

Mob

E-Mail

Name

Address

Telephone

Mob

E-Mail

Name

Address

Telephone

Mobile

E-Mail

Name

Address

Telephone

Mobile

E-Mail

Name

Address

Telephone

Mobile

E-Mail

Name	Name
Address	Address
Telephone	Telephone
Mob	Mobile
E-Mail	E-Mail
Name	Name
Address	Address
Telephone	Telephone
Mob	Mobile
E-Mail	E-Mail
Name	Name
Address	Address
Telephone	Telephone
Mob	Mobile
E-Mail	E-Mail

XYZ

Name

Address

Telephone

Mob

E-Mail

Name

Address

Telephone

Mob

E-Mail

Name

Address

Telephone

Mobile

E-Mail

Name

Address

Telephone

Mobile

E-Mail

Name

Address

Telephone

Mobile

E-Mail

Name	Name
Address	Address
Telephone	Telephone
Mob	Mobile
E-Mail	E-Mail
Name	Name
Address	Address
Telephone	Telephone
Mob	Mobile
E-Mail	E-Mail
Name	Name
Address	Address
Telephone	Telephone
Mob	Mobile
E-Mail	E-Mail

XYZ

Name

Address

Telephone

Mob

E-Mail

Name

Address

Telephone

Mobile

E-Mail

Name

Address

Telephone

Mob

E-Mail

Name

Address

Telephone

Mobile

E-Mail

Name

Address

Telephone

Mob

E-Mail

Name

Address

Telephone

Mob

E-Mail

Name

Address

Telephone

Mob

E-Mail

Name

Address

Telephone

Mobile

E-Mail

Name

Address

Telephone

Mobile

E-Mail

Name

Address

Telephone

Mobile

E-Mail

XYZ

Gifts for all Occasions

NAME	OCCASION	DATE

Gifts for all Occasions

NAME	OCCASION	DATE

NAME	OCCASION	DATE

NAME	OCCASION	DATE

Gifts for all Occasions

NAME	OCCASION	DATE

NAME	OCCASION	DATE

NAME	OCCASION	DATE

NAME	OCCASION	DATE

Gifts for all Occasions

NAME	OCCASION	DATE

NAME	OCCASION	DATE

Gifts for all Occasions

NAME	OCCASION	DATE

NAME	OCCASION	DATE

NAME	OCCASION	DATE

NAME	OCCASION	DATE

NAME	OCCASION	DATE

Gifts for all Occasions

NAME	OCCASION	DATE

NAME	OCCASION	DATE

Gifts for all
Occasions

NAME	OCCASION	DATE

Christmas Card List

NAME	YEAR	SENT	RECEIVED

NAME	YEAR	SENT	RECEIVED

NAME	YEAR	SENT	RECEIVED

NAME	YEAR	SENT	RECEIVED

NAME	YEAR	SENT	RECEIVED

NAME	YEAR	SENT	RECEIVED

Christmas
Card List

NAME	YEAR	SENT	RECEIVED

NAME	YEAR	SENT	RECEIVED

Christmas Card List

NAME	YEAR	SENT	RECEIVED

NAME	YEAR	SENT	RECEIVED

Christmas
Card List

NAME	YEAR	SENT	RECEIVED

NAME	YEAR	SENT	RECEIVED

NAME	YEAR	SENT	RECEIVED

NAME	YEAR	SENT	RECEIVED